C000258973

Playday

Story written by Gill Munton
Illustrated by Tim Archbold

Speed Sounds

Consonants   *Ask children to say the sounds.*

f ff	l ll le	m mm	n nn	r rr	s ss se ce	v ve	z zz se s	sh	(th)	(ng) (nk)

b bb	c k ck	d dd	g gg	h	j	p pp	qu	t tt	w wh	x	y	ch tch

Each box contains one sound but sometimes more than one grapheme.
*Focus graphemes for this story are **circled**.*

Vowels

Ask children to say the sounds in and out of order.

a	e ea	i	o	u	(ay)	ee y	igh	ow
at	hen	in	on	up	day	see	high	blow

oo	oo	ar	or oor ore	air	ir	ou	oy
zoo	look	car	for	fair	whirl	shout	boy

Story Green Words

Miss Jay Ben Kim Beth Pip Sam

Jess class tray clay

Ask children to say the syllables and then read the whole word.

o kay

Ask children to read the root first and then the whole word with the suffix.

dress → dressing

6

Red Words

Ask children to practise reading the words across the rows, down the columns and in and out of order clearly and quickly.

what	they	do	said
you	to	the	we
want	some	I've	all
are	your	go	no

Playday

"Okay, Class 1," said Miss Jay.
"I will tell you what you will do today.

Ben and Kim, you may play
in the sand tray."

They went to play
in the sand tray.

"Beth and Pip, you may play with the clay."

They went to play with the clay.

"Sam and Jess, you may play with the dressing up box."

They went to play with the dressing up box.

"Miss Jay," said Jess. "What will *you* do today?"

"I think *I* will play as well," said Miss Jay.

"I will play with you!"

Questions to talk about

Ask children to TTYP for each question using 'Fastest finger' (FF) or 'Have a think' (HaT).

p.8   (FF)   What is Miss Jay telling Class 1?

p.9   (FF)   Where does Miss Jay tell Ben and Kim to play?

p.10 (FF)   What does Miss Jay tell Beth and Pip to play with?

p.11 (FF)   What does Miss Jay tell Sam and Jess to play with?

p.12 (FF)   What does Jess ask Miss Jay?

p.13 (HaT)   Why do you think Miss Jay chose to play with the children?